FRACTIONS
WITH
TANGRAMS

Larry Ecklund

Didax

Order Number 2-4221
ISBN 978-1-58324-255-1

D E F G H 14 13 12 11 10

395 Main Street
Rowley, MA 01969
www.didax.com

Table of Contents

 Introduction

It is the purpose of this book to help students understand a certain kind of fractional concept – congruent regions and ONE. You will find many activities that will relate to an understanding of the part-whole situations using the TANGRAM SET.

The activities in this book are designed to provide students with hands-on situations where they will actually place tangram pieces on models of shapes and record the factional number.

In addition to working with the manipulative models of fractions as congruent regions (tangram pieces) students will gain insights and practice with the concept of fractional equivalence.

As you work through the various activities of building concepts of fractions and equivalence, please keep in mind that it will be very important to encourage students to use and handle the tangram pieces, and to do the activities with tangram pieces. Please don't fall victim to the idea of moving too rapidly through the pages of this book just to get through it.

Feel free to duplicate pages of this book for learning center activity task cards, cooperative learning projects and homework.

Complete answers for all puzzles and activities begin on page 54. You may want to review these as you explain the activities to your students.

Getting Started

Legend tells us that in ancient times a Chinese scholar possessed a very fine ceramic tile. One day, as he was taking it to show to the emperor, he slipped and dropped the tile, breaking it into seven pieces. He spent the rest of his life attempting to put it back together. This may be a well-designed story to excite the imagination, to cause speculation, or to search for further credibility.

The classic Tangram Puzzle (rebuilding the square tile) is one of the oldest and most enduring geometric puzzles. The square tile is made up of seven geometric shapes that are referred to as the seven tangram pieces:

> 2 large congruent triangles,
> 1 medium sized triangle,
> 2 small congruent triangles,
> 1 parallelogram and
> 1 square.

Tangrams have been a constant curiosity and challenge to students as they attempt to solve the classic seven-piece problem. We have included reproducible activities for you to use in the classroom with your students. Please encourage your students to "solve" the seven-piece tangram puzzles and make drawings of their solutions.

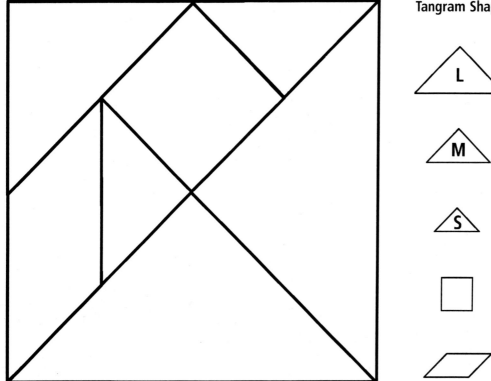

Tangram Shape Symbols:

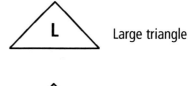

Large triangle

Medium triangle

Small triangle

Square

Parallelogram

As students work with and manipulate the tangram pieces, they learn concepts of geometry and fractions. Concepts of congruence, similarity, angles, area, shape, measurement, spatial awareness, fractional relationships, equivalence and problem solving are all valid topics to explore with these tangram puzzle pieces.

This book has been designed to help students build an understanding of fractional number concepts as they complete the various exercises and manipulate the seven tangram pieces to illustrate halves, fourths, eighths, sixteenths, thirds, sixths and their equivalents.

You will want to have several sets of tangrams for your class. You may construct tangram sets from the backline master that is included in this book, or you may purchase tangrams from your school-supply store. Eight or more sets of tangrams are recommended for each classroom or two sets for each learning center.

One or more tangram pieces will cover other tangram shapes. Covering shapes with other shapes is a basic activity that students do as they work their way through these activities. This process is a prerequisite for developing an understanding of fractional concepts with tangrams. Please encourage students to use the tangram pieces to explore and cover the various patterns, shapes and designs that are presented in these pages.

Example:

This picture of a parallelogram may be covered with the parallelogram shape itself or with two small triangles.

Each small triangle is $\frac{1}{2}$ the parallelogram.

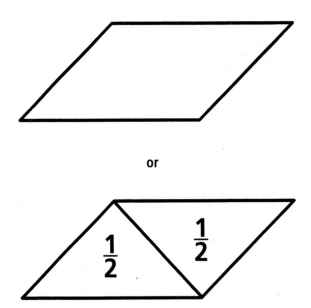

or

Throughout this book, students will be challenged to place tangram shapes on the various illustrations of other tangram shapes and identify the fractions. In the case of the parallelogram shown above, two small congruent (equal sides, equal angles, equal areas) triangles were required to cover the ONE shape.

To help students understand, it is essential that they know what the terms of the fraction mean. It is at this point that problems of understanding arise for many students.

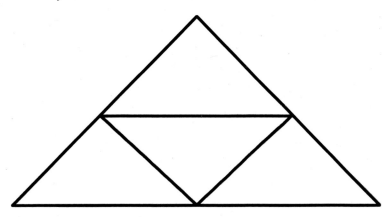

The illustration above records that four small triangles will cover the large triangle. Each of the small triangles is the same size and shape (congruent). If we pick up one of the small triangles, it represents one of the four congruent triangles; it is written as $\frac{1}{4}$. The 1 above the fraction bar is called the **numerator**, which tells us how many pieces we are considering (one of the four small triangles).

The 4 below the fraction bar is called the **denominator**, which tells us that four congruent small triangles will cover the one large triangle. The denominator functions as the *namer* of the number of congruent triangles that cover the one large triangle.

Terms of the Fraction

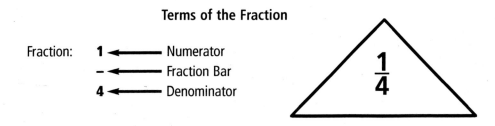

Fraction: **1** ◄———— Numerator
— ◄———— Fraction Bar
4 ◄———— Denominator

Table of Relationships:

1 large triangle	=	4 small triangles; each small triangle	=	$\frac{1}{4}$ of the large triangles.
1 large triangle	=	2 medium triangles; each of the medium triangles	=	$\frac{1}{2}$ of the triangles.
1 medium triangle	=	2 small triangles; each small triangle	=	$\frac{1}{2}$ of the medium triangle.
1 parallelogram	=	2 small triangles; each small triangle	=	$\frac{1}{2}$ of the parallelogram.
1 square	=	2 small triangles; each small triangle	=	$\frac{1}{2}$ of the square.

In this book, we will emphasize the concept of congruent regions or the area model in a hands-on mode. Each of the tangram pieces is to be used and handled by the student as they develop and strengthen their understanding of fractions.

Fractions are somewhat difficult to understand for many students because of the number arrangements, terminology and interpretations. In order to interpret and use fractions, the students must consider relationships-either between parts and wholes or between different quantities and ratios.

Fractions may be expressed as:

Part of the area of a shape or region (one of two parts of a parallelogram thought of as one of the two parts, stated as 1 of the 2 parts, and written as $\frac{1}{2}$).

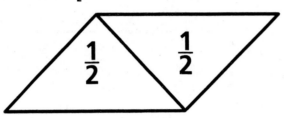

Part of a set of things (there were 4 cats out of the total of 7 pets; thought of as four of the seven pets were cats; stated as 4 of 7 pets were cats; written as $\frac{4}{7}$).

Parts of a length (a third of the distance from here to there; thought of as one of the three equal distances; stated as $\frac{1}{3}$ of a given distance; written as $\frac{1}{3}$).

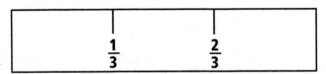

Rates (three cookies for 5¢; six cookies for 10¢; nine cookies for 15¢. These are instances of the same rate and are described as a series of ratios $\frac{3}{5}$, $\frac{6}{10}$ and $\frac{9}{15}$; thought of as 3 for 5, 6 for 10, and 9 for 15; stated as a ratio $\frac{3}{5}$, $\frac{6}{10}$ and $\frac{9}{15}$; written as $\frac{3}{5} = \frac{6}{10} = \frac{9}{15}$).

$$\frac{3}{5}$$

$$\frac{6}{10}$$

Tangrams Pieces

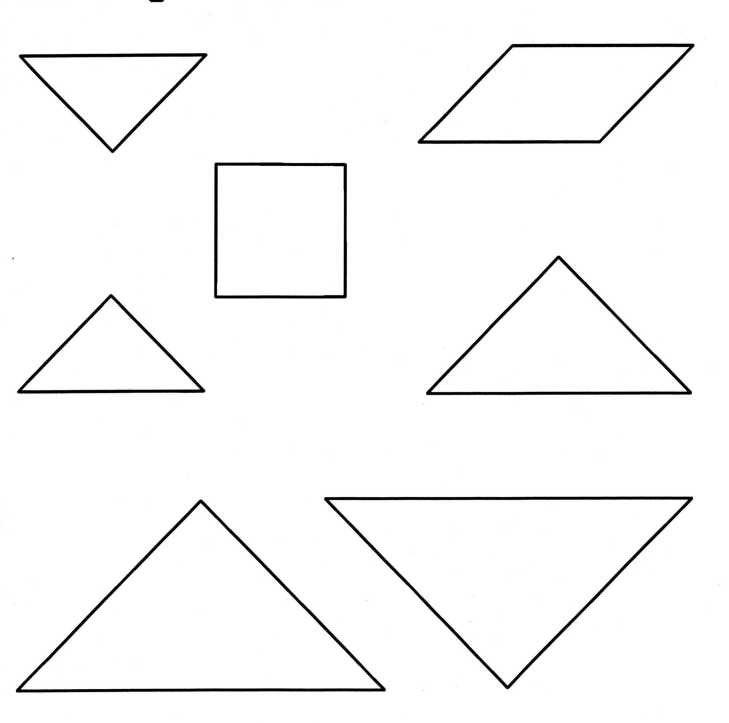

Duplicate copies of these TANGRAM PIECES for your classroom use. You may wish to duplicate these pieces on construction paper or card stock and have students cut out two or three sets for their hands-on experiences with fractions. Students may store these pieces in a small plastic bag or envelope so that they are readily available when working with the fraction activities in this book.

Challenging Tangram Puzzles

For years, children and adults have been engrossed with producing and solving tangram puzzles. Producers of tangram puzzles usually like to show the general outline of some recognizable form or figure and challenge the rest of us to fill in the forms and figures with all seven of the tangram pieces. We too would like to try our luck and present a challenge to those of you who accept puzzle challenges. Each of the puzzles presented on the following pages can be solved with the seven tangram pieces. This is to say that all seven of the tangram pieces will cover each of the following outlines of the shapes and figures. When you have finished covering the figures, please draw the lines indicating the shapes used to solve the puzzle. See our cat puzzle below.

Cover with all 7 tangram pieces and draw in the lines.

Tangram Puzzle: 2

Cover with all 7 tangram pieces and draw in the lines.

Tangram Puzzle: 3

Cover with all 7 tangram pieces and draw in the lines.

Tangram Puzzle: 4

Cover with all 7 tangram pieces and draw in the lines.

Tangram Puzzle: 5

Cover with all 7 tangram pieces and draw in the lines.

Tangram Puzzle: 6

Cover with all 7 tangram pieces and draw in the lines.

On the following pages are several geometric shapes: a square, a rectangle, a parallelogram, a trapezoid and an irregular hexagon. Please assign the task of using all seven of the tangram pieces to cover each of the lines showing the placement of each tangram piece.

Tangram Puzzle: 7

Cover with all 7 tangram pieces and draw in the lines.

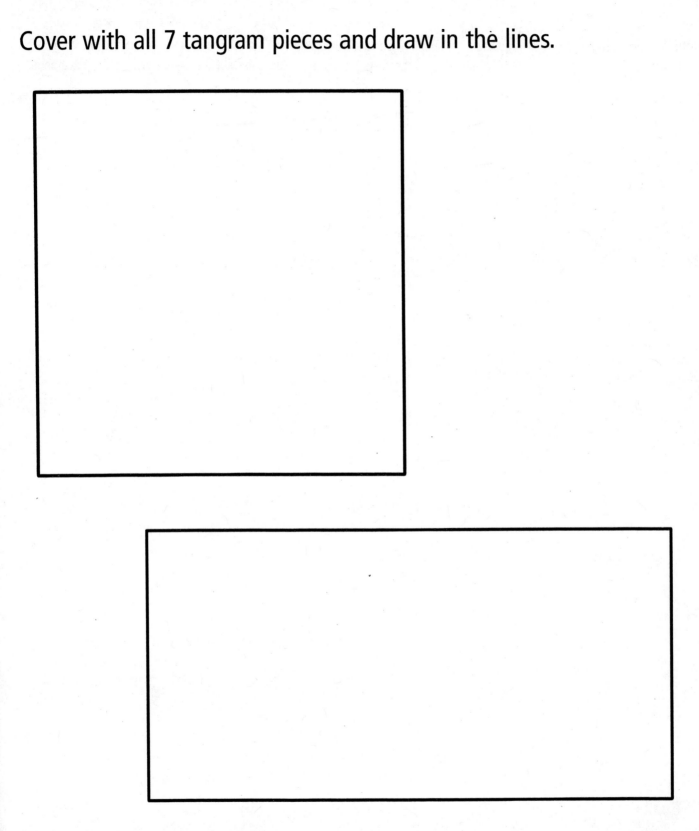

Use all 7 tangram pieces to solve the trapezoid puzzle.
Draw in the lines.

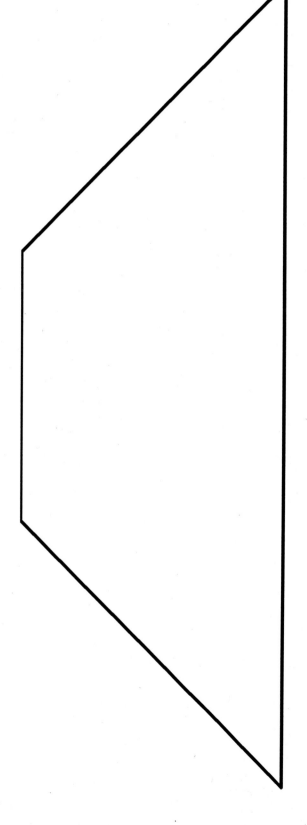

Use all 7 tangram pieces to solve the parallelogram puzzle.
Draw in the lines.

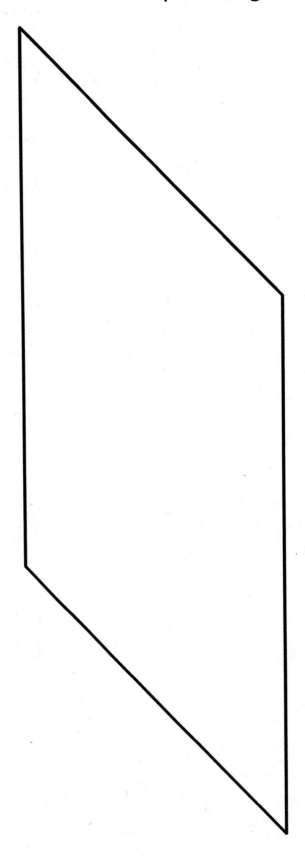

# Tangram Puzzle: 10

Use all 7 tangram pieces to solve the triangle puzzle.
Draw in the lines.

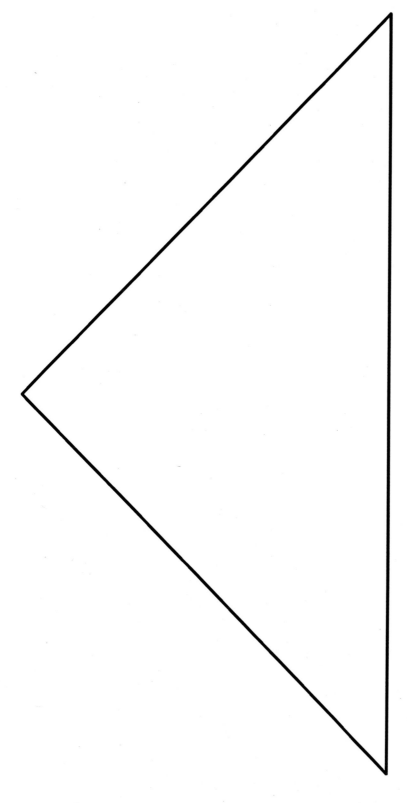

Use all 7 pieces to solve the hexagon puzzle.
Draw in the lines.

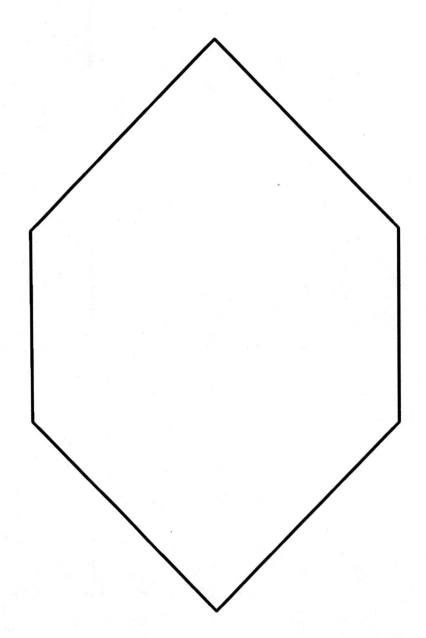

Tangram Investigation: 1

Use your tangram pieces to complete these problems.

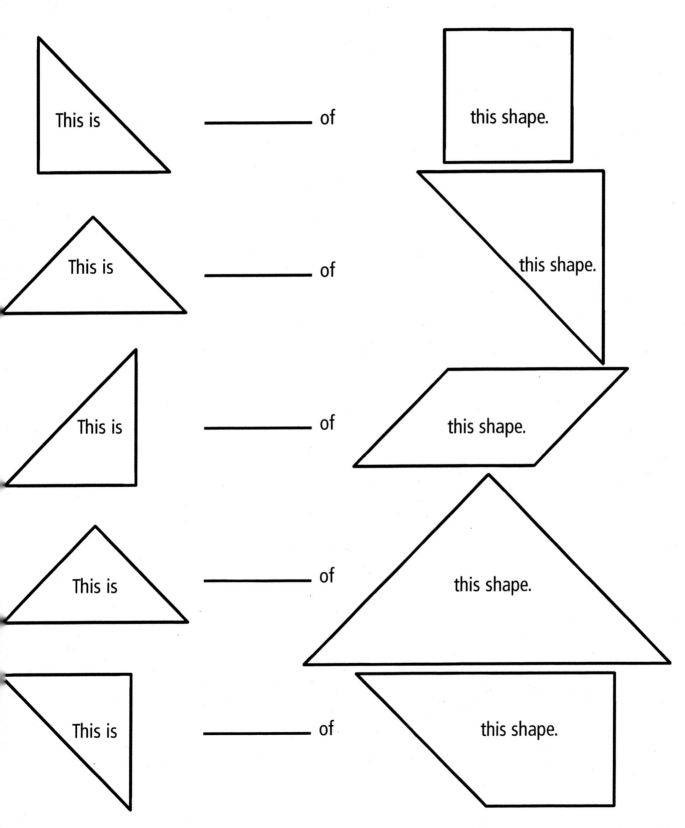

This is _____ of this shape.

This is _____ of this shape.

This is _____ of this shape.

This is _____ of this shape.

This is _____ of this shape.

Use your tangram pieces to identify these fractions.

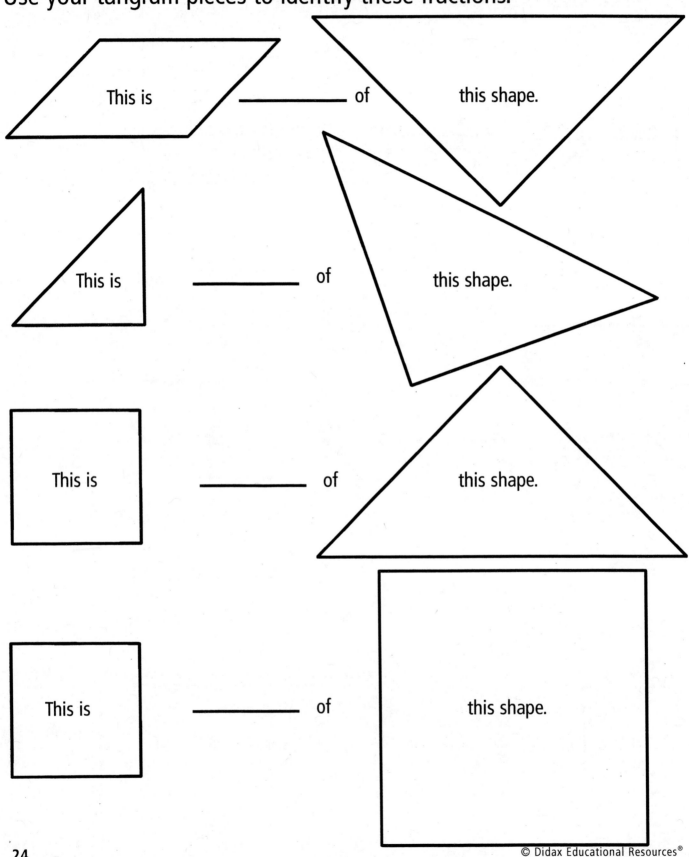

This is _____ of this shape.

This is _____ of this shape.

This is _____ of this shape.

This is _____ of this shape.

Tangram Investigation: 3

Fill each shape with two tangram pieces, name each $\frac{1}{2}$ and color one of the halves.

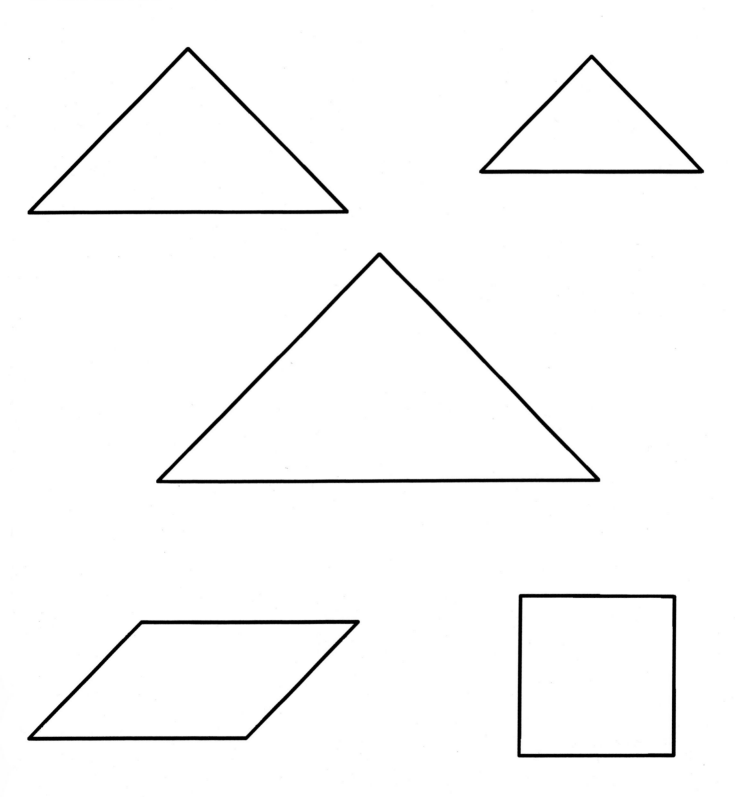

Tangram Investigation: 4

Fill each shape with four tangram pieces, name each $\frac{1}{4}$ and color one of the fourths.

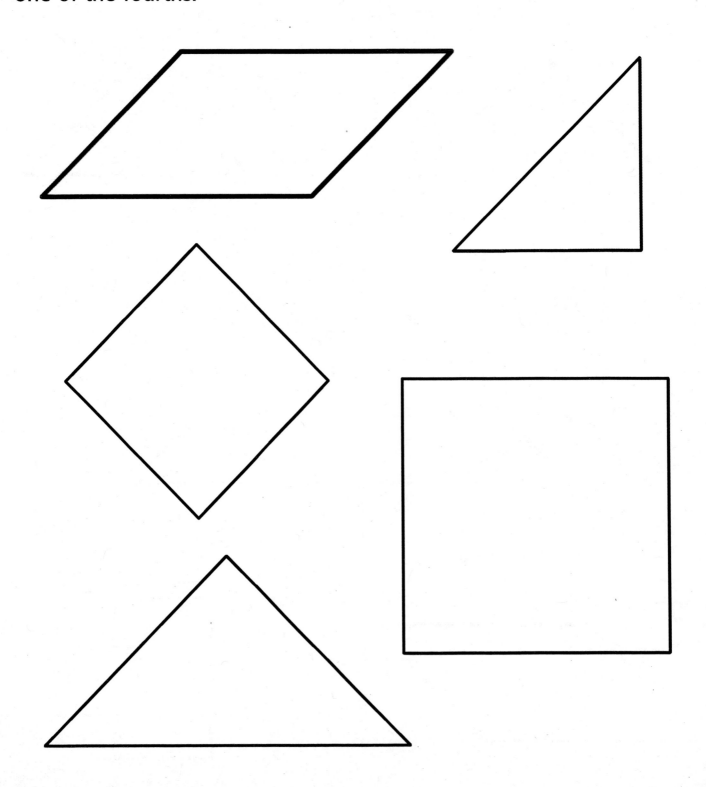

Tangram Investigation: 5

Use your tangram pieces to help identify these fractions.

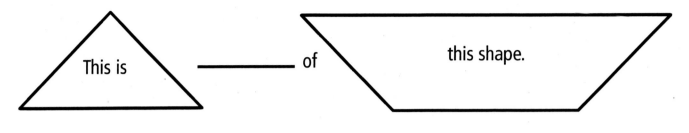

This is _____ of this shape.

This is _____ of this shape.

This is _____ of this shape.

This is _____ of this shape.

Tangram Investigation: 6

Use your tangram pieces to answer the following:

_____ = 1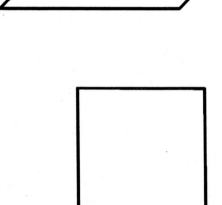

_____ = 1

_____ = 1

_____ = 1

_____ = 1

1 is _____ of

1 is _____ of

1 is _____ of

1 is _____ of

1 is _____ of

2 is _____ of

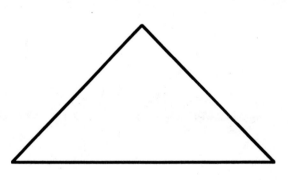

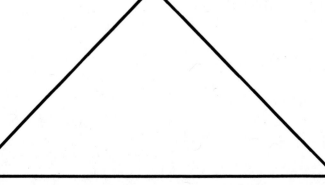

28

ONE

How many of the ☐ will cover this one square? _____

The tangram square is one part of the larger one square shown at the top of this page. Because there are four small squares that cover the one square, one small square is thought of as one of the four squares. It is written $\frac{1}{4}$.

Two of the small squares is written as $\frac{2}{4}$ and we can actually see that the two squares cover one half of the large square. We can say that the two small squares equal one half of the one square.

Write the fraction for one ☐ . _____

Write the fraction for two ☐ . _____

Write the fraction for three ☐ . _____

Write the fraction for four ☐ . _____

Another name for $\frac{2}{4}$ is _____ . $\frac{2}{4}$ = _____

Another name for $\frac{4}{2}$ is _____ . $\frac{4}{4}$ = _____

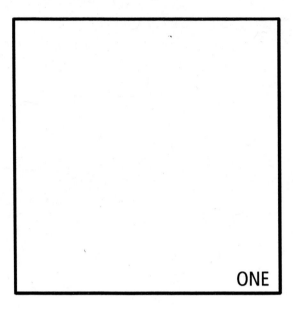

ONE

How many large triangles will cover this square? _____

Each large triangle is _____ of the square.

How many of the medium triangles will cover the square? _____

Each medium triangle is _____ of the square.

Write a fraction for 2 △M . _____

Write a fraction for 3 △M . _____

Write a fraction for 4 △M . _____

Another name for $\frac{2}{4}$ is _____ . $\frac{2}{4}$ = _____

Another name for $\frac{4}{4}$ is _____ . $\frac{4}{4}$ = _____

How many △S will fit into the one square at the top of the page? _____

Each of the △S is what part of the one square? _____

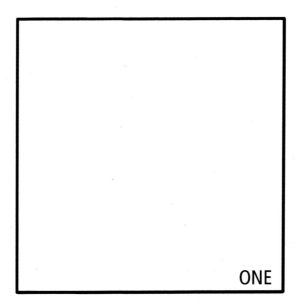

How many of the △S will cover this one square? _____

How many of the △S will cover half of the square? _____

Write the fraction for one △S . _____

Write the fraction for two △S . _____

Write the fraction for three △S . _____

Write the fraction for four △S . _____

Write the fraction for six △S . _____

Write the fraction for eight △S . _____

Another name for $\frac{2}{8}$ is _____ . $\frac{2}{8}$ = _____

Another name for $\frac{4}{8}$ is _____ . $\frac{4}{8}$ = _____

Another name for $\frac{6}{8}$ is _____ . $\frac{6}{8}$ = _____

Another name for $\frac{8}{8}$ is _____ . $\frac{8}{8}$ = _____

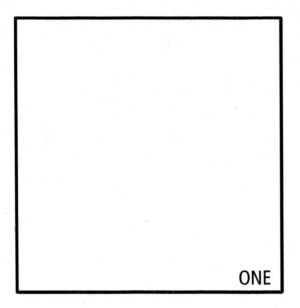

ONE

Cover the ONE square with these tangram shapes and draw the line placement of the pieces.

Take:

1 ☐ square

1 ▱ parallelogram

1 △M Medium triangle

2 △S small triangles

1 ☐ covers _____ of the ONE.

1 ▱ covers _____ of the ONE.

2 △S covers _____ of the ONE.

1 △M covers _____ of the ONE.

1 △S covers _____ of the ONE.

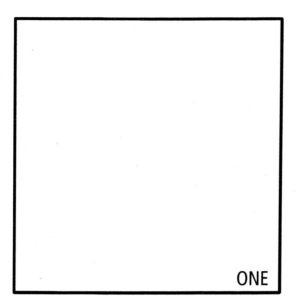

ONE

Cover the ONE square with these tangram pieces, draw in the shapes and answer the questions below.

Take:

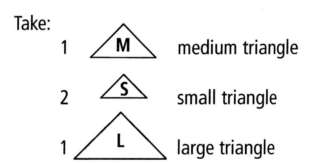

1   M   medium triangle

2   S   small triangle

1   L   large triangle

1   L   covers what part of the ONE? _____

1   M   covers what part of the ONE? _____

1   S   covers what part of the ONE? _____

2   S   covers what part of the ONE? _____

1   S   covers what part of 1   L   ? _____

2   M   covers what part of 1   L   ? _____

Use your tangram pieces to complete this activity.

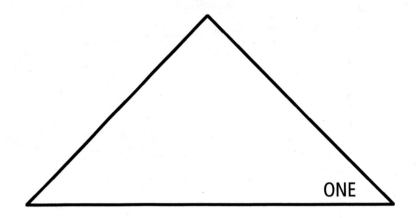

1. How many △M̱ will cover this triangle? _____

2. Each △M̱ is_____ of ONE.

3. How many △S̱ will cover ONE? _____

4. Each △S̱ is_____ of ONE.

5. Two △S̱ = _____ of ONE.

6. Three △S̱ = _____ of ONE.

7. One ☐ = _____ of ONE.

8. One ▱ = _____ of ONE.

Use your tangram pieces to complete this activity.

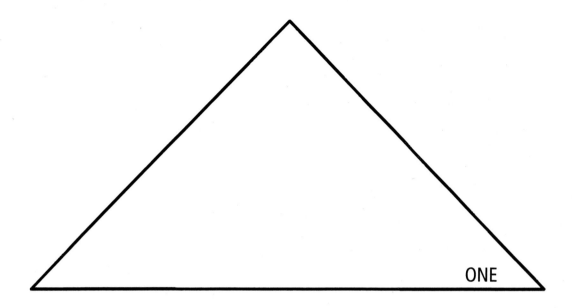

1. How many /L\ will cover ONE? _____   Each /L\ is_____ of ONE.

2. How many /M\ will cover ONE? _____   Each /M\ is_____ of ONE.

3. How many /S\ will cover ONE? _____   Each /S\ is_____ of ONE.

4. Two /M\ will cover_____ of ONE.

5. Three /M\ will cover_____ of ONE.

6. Four /S\ will cover_____ of ONE.

Use your tangram pieces to complete this activity.

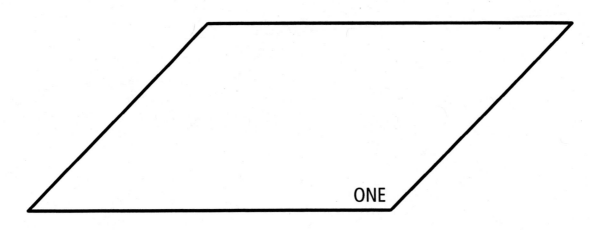

ONE

1. How many L will cover this parallelogram? _____

2. Each L is _____ of ONE.

3. How many ⟋⟋ will cover ONE? _____

4. Each ⟋⟋ is _____ of ONE.

5. Two ⟋⟋ = _____ of ONE.

6. Three ⟋⟋ = _____ of ONE.

7. One M = _____ of ONE.

8. Two M = _____ of ONE.

9. Four S = _____ of ONE.

10. Another name for four S is _____ .

Build these shapes, draw in the lines and complete the information.

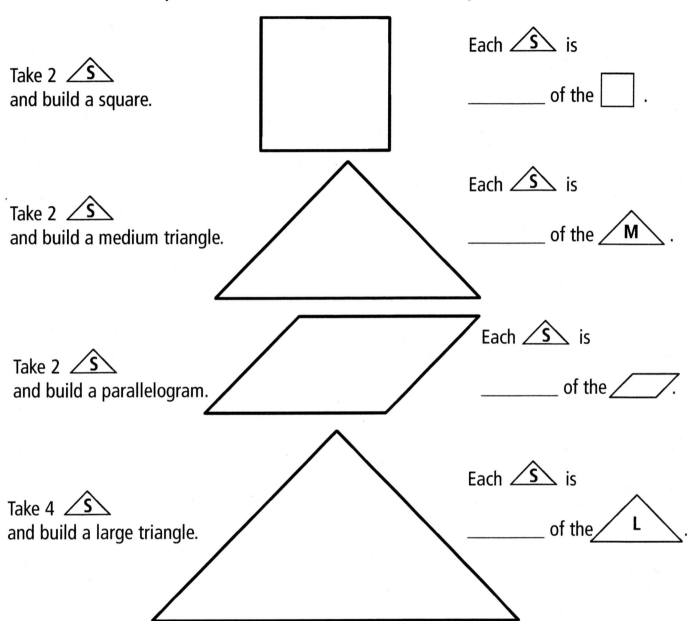

Take 2 △S and build a square.

Each △S is _____ of the ▢ .

Take 2 △S and build a medium triangle.

Each △S is _____ of the △M .

Take 2 △S and build a parallelogram.

Each △S is _____ of the ▱.

Take 4 △S and build a large triangle.

Each △S is _____ of the △L .

Do you see a square in the large triangle? _____

The square is what part of the △L ? _____

Do you see a parallelogram in the large triangle? _____

What part of the large triangle is the parallelogram? _____

More Investigations: 2

Build these shapes, draw in the lines and complete the information.

Take 2 ◢M◣ and build a large triangle.

Each ◢M◣ is _____ of the ◢L◣ .

1 ◢M◣ = _____ of the ◢L◣ .

2 ◢M◣ = _____ of the ◢L◣ .

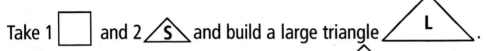

Take 1 ☐ and 2 ◢S◣ and build a large triangle ◢L◣ .

1 ☐ and 2 ◢S◣ = _____ of the ◢L◣ .

1 ☐ = _____ of the ◢L◣ .

1 ◢S◣ = _____ of the ◢L◣ .

2 ◢S◣ = _____ of the ◢L◣ .

Take 1 ▱ and 2 ◢S◣ and fill in a large triangle ◢L◣ .

1 ▱ = _____ of the ◢L◣ .

1 ◢S◣ = _____ of the ◢L◣ .

2 ◢S◣ = _____ of the ◢L◣ .

Problem Solving: Introduction

In the next series of activities, please encourage the students to use their tangram pieces to experiment with the sizes and shapes of the various tangram pieces shown below. If you do not have enough of the commercial tangram pieces available please use the "tangram cut out" patterns included in this book.

Students should be encouraged to check the relationships of a given shape to another shape or shapes. Please keep in mind that students should see, handle, manipulate and identity the fractional parts of ONE. *One is any unit of our choosing.* We will also ask questions relating one tangram piece to another.

The tangram pieces are identical in three ways:

Letters of the Alphabet		**Symbols**	**Fractions**
A	Identifies the medium triangle	M (triangle)	$\frac{1}{8}$
B	Identifies the Square	□ (square)	$\frac{1}{8}$
C & E	Identify the two small triangles	S (triangle)	$\frac{1}{16}$ each
F & G	Identify the two large triangles	L (triangle)	$\frac{1}{4}$ each
D	Identifies the parallegram	▱ (parallelogram)	$\frac{1}{8}$

Triangles **G** and **F** equal half of the ONE square

Shapes **A**, **B**, **C**, **D** and **E** equal half of the ONE square.

Use this tangram puzzle solution to answer questions about the tangram shapes and fractions on the following pages. Letters, symbols and fractions are used to identify the shapes.

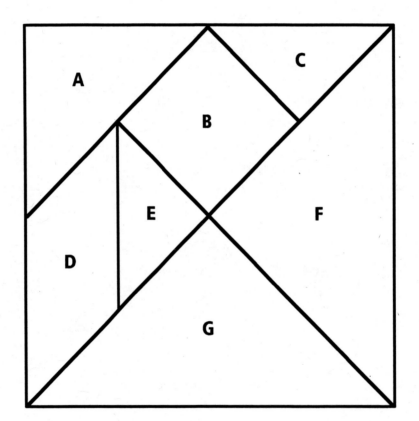

Problem Solving: 1

Refer to ONE on the previous page, use your tangram pieces and complete the following:

1. How many **F**'s fill ONE? _____   **F** is _____ of ONE.

2. How many **G**'s fill ONE? _____   **G** is _____ of ONE.

3. How many **C**'s fill ONE? _____   **C** is _____ of ONE.

4. How many **E**'s fill ONE? _____   **E** is _____ of ONE.

5. How many **A**'s fill ONE? _____   **A** is _____ of ONE.

6. **G** and **F** equal _____ of ONE.

7. **A**, **B**, **C**, **D** and **E** equal _____ of ONE.

8. **C** is _____ of **B**.

9. **C** is _____ of **F**.

10. **C** is _____ of **A**.

11. **E** is _____ of **D**.

12. **E** is _____ of **B**.

13. **D** is _____ of **G**.

14. **C**, **D** and **E** are _____ of ONE.

Problem Solving: 2

Use the 7 tangram pieces to answer the following questions.

1. The triangle shapes are _____, _____,_____,_____ and _____.

2. The square shape is _____.

3. The parallelogram shape is _____.

4. How do triangles **G** and **F** compare? _____

_____

5. How do triangles **C** and **E** compare? _____

_____

6. Draw tangrams **A**, **B** and **D** using triangles **C** and **E** in the space below.

A   **B**

D

Problem Solving: 3

Use the 7 tangram pieces to complete the following activities:

1. How many of the **C** shapes fit into the **F** shape? _____

2. Would the same number of **E** shapes fit into the **G** shape? _____

   How do you know?_____

   _____

3. How would you "build" **F** or **G** by using **B**? You may use other tangram pieces to complete this task. Please show your work.

4. How would you "build" **F** or **G** by using **D** and other tangram pieces? You may use other tangram pieces to complete this task. Please show your work.

Problem Solving: 4

Draw a square by using the two triangle pieces G and F and label it ONE.

1. How many square tangram pieces will fit into this square? _____

   Each square is _____ of ONE.

2. Use shapes **A** and **D** in the square. What other shape or shapes will be needed to fill

   in the square? _____

   _____

3. **D** and **A** cover what part of ONE? _____

4. How many **C**'s and **E**'s will cover ONE? _____

5. How many **C**'s would cover $\frac{1}{2}$ of ONE? _____

Problem Solving: 5

Use your tangram pieces and complete the following:

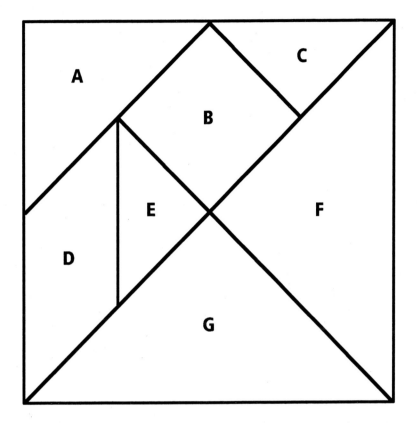

1. If there are 2 **C**'s in **A**, then there are _____ **E**'s in **A**.

2. If there are 2 **A**'s in **F**, then there are _____ **A**'s in **G**.

3. If there are 4 **E**'s in **G**, then there are_____ **E**'s in **F**.

4. If there are 4 **C**'s in **F**, then there are _____ **C**'s in **G**.

5. How many more **C**'s are in **F** than in **G**? _____

6. How many more **E**'s are in **A** than in **C**? _____

7. How many more **A**'s are in ONE than in **G**? _____

Problem Solving: 6

Use your tangram pieces and complete the following:

1. **E** is what part of **C**? _____

2. **B** is what part of **F**? _____

3. **G** is what part of ONE? _____

4. **A** is what part of **G** and **F**? _____

5. **E** is what part of **G** and **F**? _____

6. How many **C**'s are in **A**? _____   **C** is _____ of **A**.

7. How many **C**'s are in **B**? _____   **C** is _____ of **B**.

8. How many **C**'s are in **D**? _____   **C** is _____ of **D**.

9. How many **C**'s are in **E**? _____   **C** is _____ of **E**.

10. How many **C**'s are in **F**? _____   **C** is _____ of **F**.

11. How many **C**'s are in **G**? _____   **C** is _____ of **G**.

12. How many **C**'s are in ONE? _____   **C** is _____ of ONE.

13. How many **A**'s are in **F**? _____   **A** is _____ of **F**.

14. How many **A**'s are in **G**? _____   **A** is _____ of **G**.

15. How many **A**'s are in ONE? _____   **A** is _____ of ONE.

16. How many **F**'s are in ONE? _____   **F** is _____ of ONE.

Problem Solving: 7

Use the small triangle  as the tangram unit to "measure" and
name the fractions and their equivalence.

$$1 \, \triangle_S = \frac{1}{16}$$

1. Triangle **A** = _____ .
    16

2. Triangle **C** = _____ .
    16

3. Square **B** = _____ .
    16

4. Parallelogram **D** = _____ .
    16

5. Triangle **E** = _____ .
    16

6. Triangle **F** = _____ .
    16

7. Triangle **G** = _____ .
    16

8. Triangle **G** also = _____ and _____ .
    8 4

9. Triangle **F** also = _____ and _____ .
    8 4

10. Triangle **A** also = _____ .
     8

11. Square **B** also = _____ .
     8

12. Parallelogram **D** = _____ .
     8

13. ONE = _____ .
     16

Use your tangram shapes to answer these questions.

ONE

1. How many large triangles ◿L will cover ONE? _____

   Please draw each large triangle in ONE.

2. How many large triangles ◿L cover $\frac{1}{2}$ of ONE? _____

   Please color $\frac{1}{2}$ of ONE.

3. How many large triangles ◿L cover $\frac{1}{4}$ of ONE? _____

   Please color $\frac{1}{4}$ of ONE another color.

4. How many of the large triangles are colored? _____

5. How many of the large triangles are not colored? _____

This is One: 2

Use your tangram shapes to answer these questions.

ONE

1. How many medium triangles /M\ will cover ONE? _____

   Please draw each medium triangle in ONE.

2. How many medium triangles /M\ cover $\frac{1}{2}$ of ONE? _____

   Please color $\frac{1}{2}$ of ONE. $\frac{1}{2} =$ _____
                                                              8

3. How many medium triangles /M\ cover $\frac{1}{4}$ of ONE? _____

   Please color $\frac{1}{4}$ of ONE another color. $\frac{1}{4} =$ _____
                                                                     8

4. How many of the medium triangles are colored? _____ = _____
                                                                          8

5. How many of the medium triangles are not colored? _____ = _____
                                                                        8

49

Use your tangram shapes to answer these questions.

ONE

1. How many small triangles  S will cover ONE? _____

   Please draw each small triangle in ONE.

2. How many small triangles S will cover $\frac{1}{2}$ of ONE? _____

   Please color $\frac{1}{2}$ of ONE. $\qquad$ $\frac{1}{2} = \underline{\hspace{1cm}} = \underline{\hspace{1cm}} = \underline{\hspace{1cm}}$
   $\phantom{\frac{1}{2} =}\ \ 16 \qquad\ \ 8 \qquad\ \ 4$

3. How many small triangles S will cover $\frac{1}{4}$ of ONE? _____

   Please color $\frac{1}{4}$ of ONE another color. $\frac{1}{4} = \underline{\hspace{1cm}} = \underline{\hspace{1cm}}$
   $\phantom{\frac{1}{4} =}\ \ 16 \qquad\ \ 8$

4. How many of the small triangles are colored? $\underline{\hspace{1cm}} = \underline{\hspace{1cm}} = \underline{\hspace{1cm}} = \underline{\hspace{1cm}}$
   $16 \qquad 8 \qquad 4$

5. How many of the small triangles are not colored? $\underline{\hspace{1cm}} = \underline{\hspace{1cm}} = \underline{\hspace{1cm}} = \underline{\hspace{1cm}}$
   $16 \qquad 8 \qquad 4$

This is One: 4

Use your tangram shapes to answer these questions.

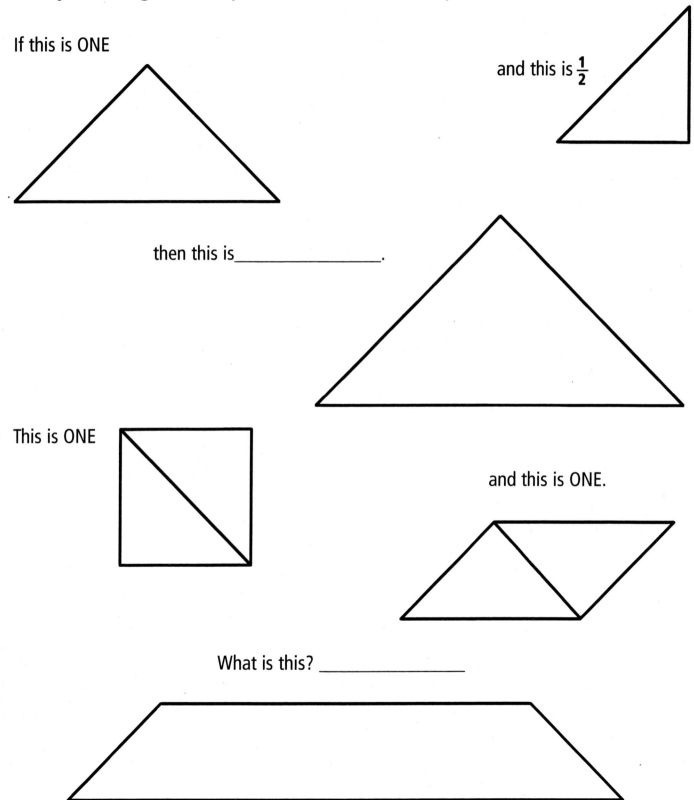

If this is ONE

and this is $\frac{1}{2}$

then this is_____.

This is ONE

and this is ONE.

What is this? _____

This is One: 5

Use your tangram shapes to answer these questions.

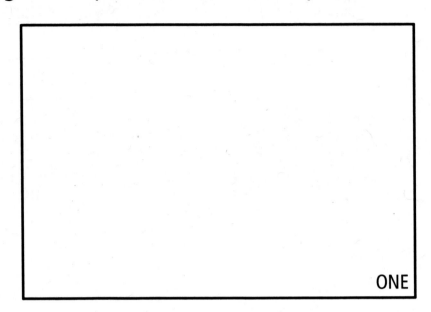

ONE

1. How many ☐ will cover ONE? _____

2 ☐ cover_____.

2. How many △S△ will cover ONE? _____

6 △S△ cover_____.

3. How many ☐ will cover $\frac{1}{2}$ of ONE? _____

4. How many ☐ will cover $\frac{1}{3}$ of ONE? _____

5. How many ☐ will cover $\frac{2}{3}$ of ONE? _____

6. $\frac{1}{2}$ of ONE is how many △S△ ? _____

7. $\frac{1}{3}$ of ONE is how many △S△ ? _____

1 This is One: 6

Use your tangram pieces and name these fractions:

8. Each ⟋S⟍ is what part of ONE? _____

9. Each ☐ is what part of ONE? _____

10. Two ⟋S⟍ are equal to what part of ONE? _____

11. Three ☐ are equal to what part of ONE? _____

12. Please look at ONE and rename these fractions.

　　a. $\frac{3}{6}$ is another name for _____.

　　b. $\frac{2}{6}$ is another name for _____.

　　c. $\frac{4}{12}$ is another name for _____.

　　d. $\frac{6}{12}$ is another name for _____.

　　e. $\frac{1}{6} = \dfrac{}{12}$

　　f. $\frac{3}{6} = \dfrac{}{12}$

　　g. $\frac{4}{12} = \dfrac{}{6}$

　　h. $\frac{1}{2} = \dfrac{}{12} = \dfrac{}{6}$

　　i. $\frac{1}{3} = \dfrac{}{6} = \dfrac{}{12}$

　　j. $\frac{2}{3} = \dfrac{}{6} = \dfrac{}{12}$

　　k. $\frac{6}{6} = \dfrac{}{12}$

Tangram Solutions

Page 11

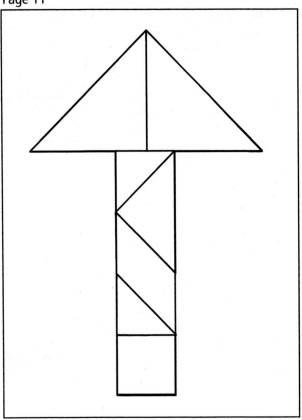

Page 12

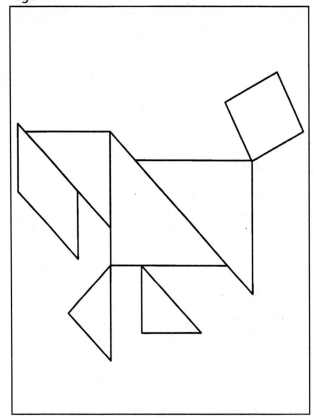

Page 13

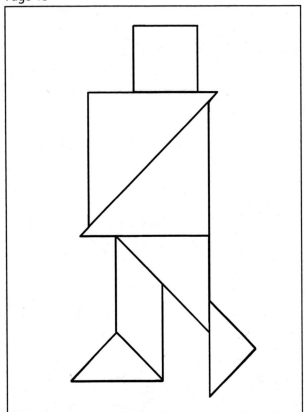

Page 14

Tangram Solutions

Page 15

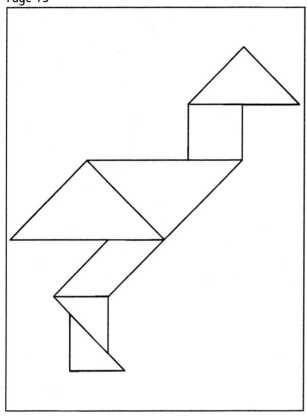

Page 16

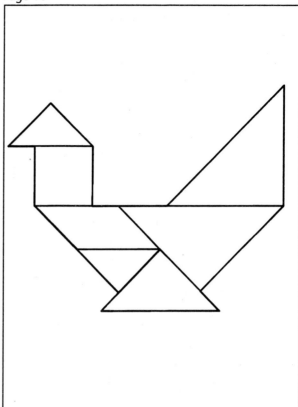

Page 17

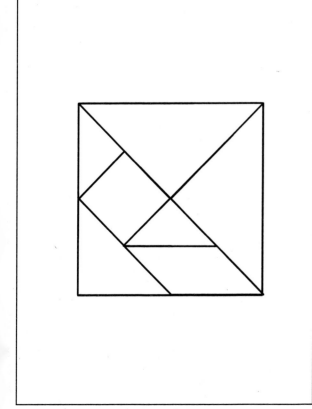

Page 18

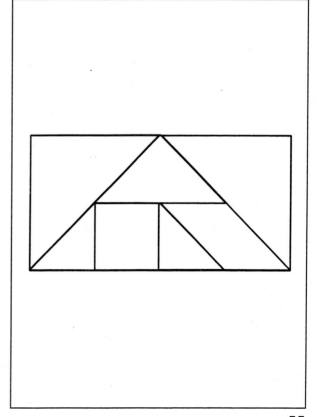

Tangram Solutions

Page 19

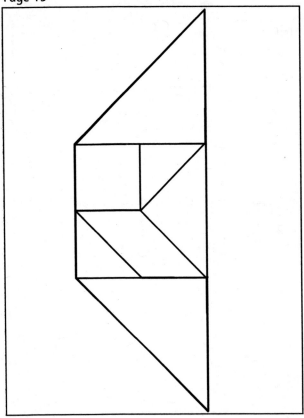

Page 20

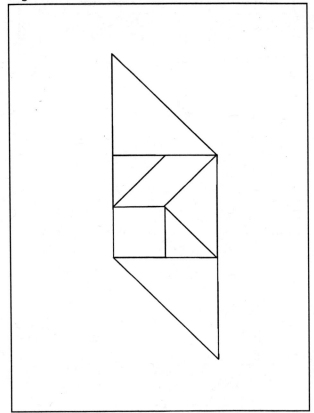

Page 21

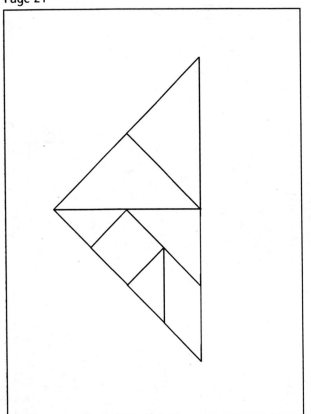

Page 22

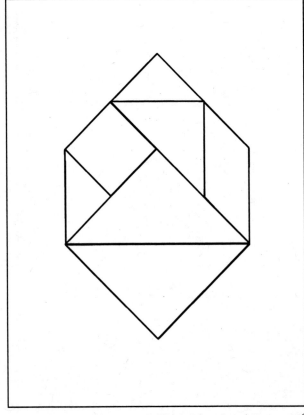

Page 23

Tangram Investigation: 1

Use your tangram pieces to complete these problems.

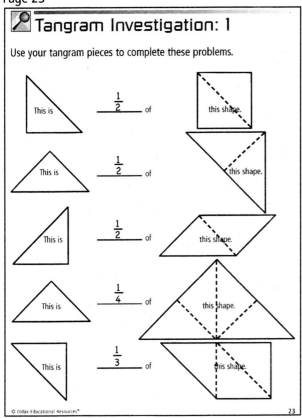

Page 24

Tangram Investigation: 2

Use your tangram pieces to identify these fractions.

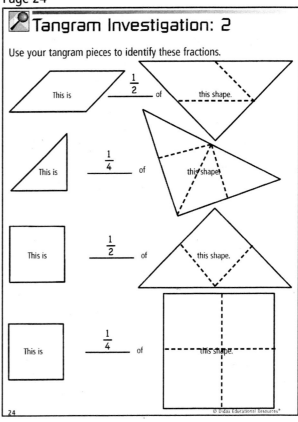

Page 25

Tangram Investigation: 3

Fill each shape with two tangram pieces, name each $\frac{1}{2}$ and color one of the halves.

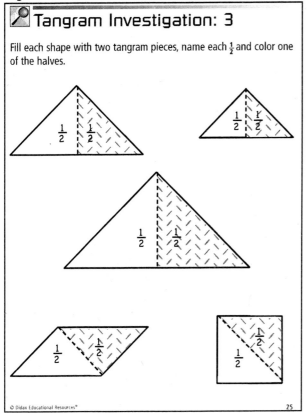

Page 26

Tangram Investigation: 4

Fill each shape with four tangram pieces, name each $\frac{1}{4}$ and color one of the fourths.

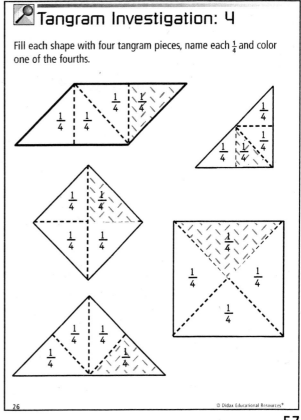

Tangram Solutions

Page 27

🔍 Tangram Investigation: 5

Use your tangram pieces to help identify these fractions.

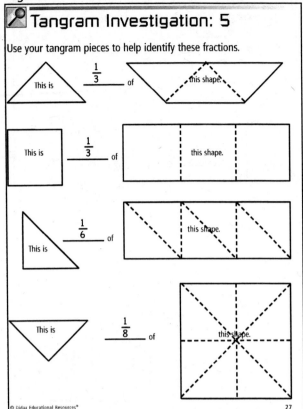

Page 28

🔍 Tangram Investigation: 6

Use your tangram pieces to answer the following:

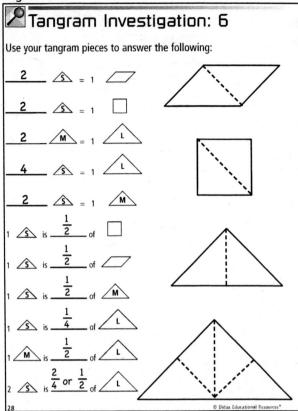

Page 29

1️⃣ Parts of One: 1

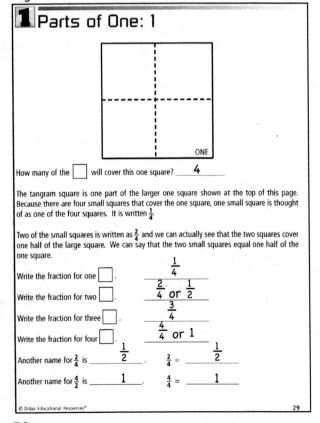

How many of the ☐ will cover this one square? __4__

The tangram square is one part of the larger one square shown at the top of this page. Because there are four small squares that cover the one square, one small square is thought of as one of the four squares. It is written $\frac{1}{4}$.

Two of the small squares is written as $\frac{2}{4}$ and we can actually see that the two squares cover one half of the large square. We can say that the two small squares equal one half of the one square.

Write the fraction for one ☐ . $\frac{1}{4}$

Write the fraction for two ☐ . $\frac{2}{4}$ or $\frac{1}{2}$

Write the fraction for three ☐ . $\frac{3}{4}$

Write the fraction for four ☐ . $\frac{4}{4}$ or 1

Another name for $\frac{2}{4}$ is __$\frac{1}{2}$__ . $\frac{2}{4}$ = __$\frac{1}{2}$__

Another name for $\frac{4}{4}$ is __1__ . $\frac{4}{4}$ = __1__

Page 30

1️⃣ Parts of One: 2

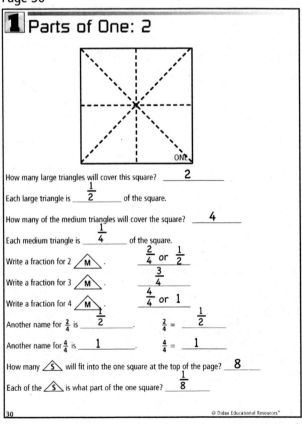

How many large triangles will cover this square? __2__

Each large triangle is __$\frac{1}{2}$__ of the square.

How many of the medium triangles will cover the square? __4__

Each medium triangle is __$\frac{1}{4}$__ of the square.

Write a fraction for 2 △M . $\frac{2}{4}$ or $\frac{1}{2}$

Write a fraction for 3 △M . $\frac{3}{4}$

Write a fraction for 4 △M . $\frac{4}{4}$ or 1

Another name for $\frac{2}{4}$ is __$\frac{1}{2}$__ . $\frac{2}{4}$ = __$\frac{1}{2}$__

Another name for $\frac{4}{4}$ is __1__ . $\frac{4}{4}$ = __1__

How many △S will fit into the one square at the top of the page? __8__

Each of the △S is what part of the one square? __$\frac{1}{8}$__

Page 31

1 Parts of One: 3

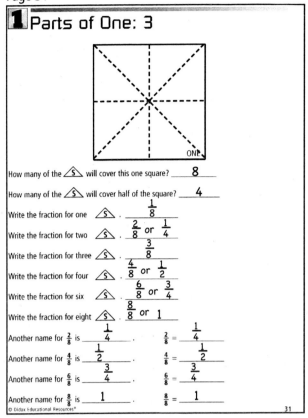

How many of the △S will cover this one square? __8__

How many of the △S will cover half of the square? __4__

Write the fraction for one △S . $\frac{1}{8}$

Write the fraction for two △S . $\frac{2}{8}$ or $\frac{1}{4}$

Write the fraction for three △S . $\frac{3}{8}$

Write the fraction for four △S . $\frac{4}{8}$ or $\frac{1}{2}$

Write the fraction for six △S . $\frac{6}{8}$ or $\frac{3}{4}$

Write the fraction for eight △S . $\frac{8}{8}$ or 1

Another name for $\frac{2}{8}$ is $\frac{1}{4}$. $\frac{2}{8} = \frac{1}{4}$

Another name for $\frac{4}{8}$ is $\frac{1}{2}$. $\frac{4}{8} = \frac{1}{2}$

Another name for $\frac{6}{8}$ is $\frac{3}{4}$. $\frac{6}{8} = \frac{3}{4}$

Another name for $\frac{8}{8}$ is 1 . $\frac{8}{8}$ = 1

© Didax Educational Resources®   31

Page 32

1 Parts of One: 4

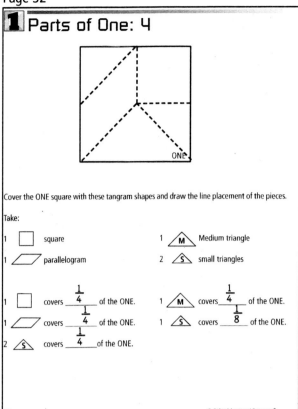

Cover the ONE square with these tangram shapes and draw the line placement of the pieces.

Take:

1 ▢ square

1 ▱ parallelogram

1 △M Medium triangle

2 △S small triangles

1 ▢ covers $\frac{1}{4}$ of the ONE.

1 ▱ covers $\frac{1}{4}$ of the ONE.

2 △S covers $\frac{1}{4}$ of the ONE.

1 △M covers $\frac{1}{4}$ of the ONE.

1 △S covers $\frac{1}{8}$ of the ONE.

© Didax Educational Resources®

Page 33

1 Parts of One: 5

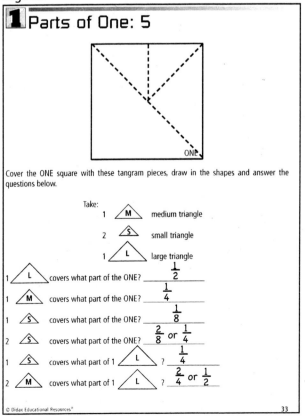

Cover the ONE square with these tangram pieces, draw in the shapes and answer the questions below.

Take:

1 △M medium triangle

2 △S small triangle

1 △L large triangle

1 △L covers what part of the ONE? $\frac{1}{2}$

1 △M covers what part of the ONE? $\frac{1}{4}$

1 △S covers what part of the ONE? $\frac{1}{8}$

2 △S covers what part of the ONE? $\frac{2}{8}$ or $\frac{1}{4}$

1 △S covers what part of 1 △L ? $\frac{1}{4}$

2 △M covers what part of 1 △L ? $\frac{2}{4}$ or $\frac{1}{2}$

© Didax Educational Resources®   33

Page 34

1 Parts of One: 6

Use your tangram pieces to complete this activity.

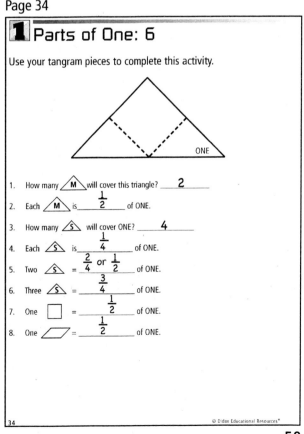

1. How many △M will cover this triangle? __2__

2. Each △M is $\frac{1}{2}$ of ONE.

3. How many △S will cover ONE? __4__

4. Each △S is $\frac{1}{4}$ of ONE.

5. Two △S = $\frac{2}{4}$ or $\frac{1}{2}$ of ONE.

6. Three △S = $\frac{3}{4}$ of ONE.

7. One ▢ = $\frac{1}{2}$ of ONE.

8. One ▱ = $\frac{1}{2}$ of ONE.

© Didax Educational Resources®

Tangram Solutions

Page 35

Page 35

1 Parts of One: 7

Use your tangram pieces to complete this activity.

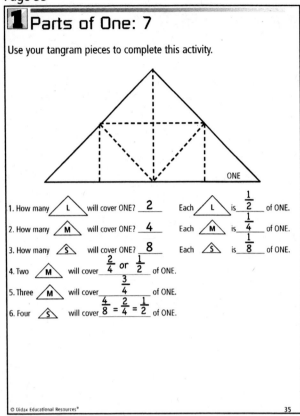

1. How many ⟨L⟩ will cover ONE? __2__   Each ⟨L⟩ is $\frac{1}{2}$ of ONE.

2. How many ⟨M⟩ will cover ONE? __4__   Each ⟨M⟩ is $\frac{1}{4}$ of ONE.

3. How many ⟨S⟩ will cover ONE? __8__   Each ⟨S⟩ is $\frac{1}{8}$ of ONE.

4. Two ⟨M⟩ will cover $\frac{2}{4}$ or $\frac{1}{2}$ of ONE.

5. Three ⟨M⟩ will cover $\frac{3}{4}$ of ONE.

6. Four ⟨S⟩ will cover $\frac{4}{8} = \frac{2}{4} = \frac{1}{2}$ of ONE.

Page 36

Page 36

1 Parts of One: 8

Use your tangram pieces to complete this activity.

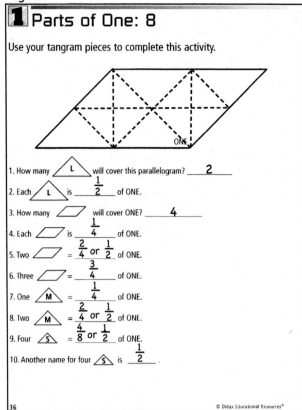

1. How many ⟨L⟩ will cover this parallelogram? __2__

2. Each ⟨L⟩ is $\frac{1}{2}$ of ONE.

3. How many ⟨▱⟩ will cover ONE? __4__

4. Each ⟨▱⟩ is $\frac{1}{4}$ of ONE.

5. Two ⟨▱⟩ = $\frac{2}{4}$ or $\frac{1}{2}$ of ONE.

6. Three ⟨▱⟩ = $\frac{3}{4}$ of ONE.

7. One ⟨M⟩ = $\frac{1}{4}$ of ONE.

8. Two ⟨M⟩ = $\frac{2}{4}$ or $\frac{1}{2}$ of ONE.

9. Four ⟨S⟩ = $\frac{4}{8}$ or $\frac{1}{2}$ of ONE.

10. Another name for four ⟨S⟩ is $\frac{1}{2}$.

Page 37

Page 37

🔍 More Investigations: 1

Build these shapes, draw in the lines and complete the information.

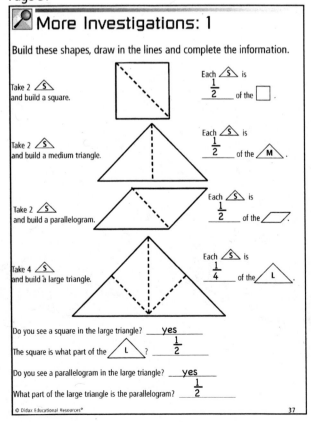

Take 2 ⟨S⟩ and build a square.

Each ⟨S⟩ is $\frac{1}{2}$ of the ⟨□⟩.

Take 2 ⟨S⟩ and build a medium triangle.

Each ⟨S⟩ is $\frac{1}{2}$ of the ⟨M⟩.

Take 2 ⟨S⟩ and build a parallelogram.

Each ⟨S⟩ is $\frac{1}{2}$ of the ⟨▱⟩.

Take 4 ⟨S⟩ and build a large triangle.

Each ⟨S⟩ is $\frac{1}{4}$ of the ⟨L⟩.

Do you see a square in the large triangle? __yes__

The square is what part of the ⟨L⟩? $\frac{1}{2}$

Do you see a parallelogram in the large triangle? __yes__

What part of the large triangle is the parallelogram? $\frac{1}{2}$

Page 38

Page 38

🔍 More Investigations: 2

Build these shapes, draw in the lines and complete the information.

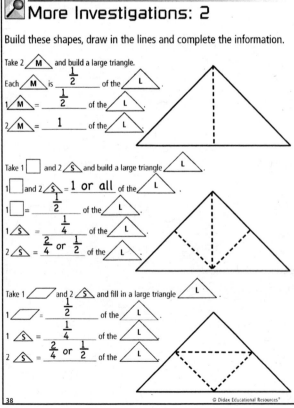

Take 2 ⟨M⟩ and build a large triangle.

Each ⟨M⟩ is $\frac{1}{2}$ of the ⟨L⟩.

1 ⟨M⟩ = $\frac{1}{2}$ of the ⟨L⟩.

2 ⟨M⟩ = 1 of the ⟨L⟩.

Take 1 ⟨□⟩ and 2 ⟨S⟩ and build a large triangle ⟨L⟩.

1 ⟨□⟩ and 2 ⟨S⟩ = 1 or all of the ⟨L⟩.

1 ⟨□⟩ = $\frac{1}{2}$ of the ⟨L⟩.

1 ⟨S⟩ = $\frac{1}{4}$ of the ⟨L⟩.

2 ⟨S⟩ = $\frac{2}{4}$ or $\frac{1}{2}$ of the ⟨L⟩.

Take 1 ⟨▱⟩ and 2 ⟨S⟩ and fill in a large triangle ⟨L⟩.

1 ⟨▱⟩ = $\frac{1}{2}$ of the ⟨L⟩.

1 ⟨S⟩ = $\frac{1}{4}$ of the ⟨L⟩.

2 ⟨S⟩ = $\frac{2}{4}$ or $\frac{1}{2}$ of the ⟨L⟩.

Tangram Solutions

Page 41

 ### Problem Solving: 1

Refer to ONE on the previous page, use your tangram pieces and complete the following:

1. How many F's fill ONE? __4__   F is $\frac{1}{4}$ of ONE.

2. How many G's fill ONE? __4__   G is $\frac{1}{4}$ of ONE.

3. How many C's fill ONE? __16__   C is $\frac{1}{16}$ of ONE.

4. How many E's fill ONE? __16__   E is $\frac{1}{16}$ of ONE.

5. How many A's fill ONE? __8__   A is $\frac{1}{8}$ of ONE.

6. G and F equal $\frac{1}{2}$ of ONE.

7. A, B, C, D and E equal $\frac{1}{2}$ of ONE.

8. C is $\frac{1}{2}$ of B.

9. C is $\frac{1}{4}$ of F.

10. C is $\frac{1}{2}$ of A.

11. E is $\frac{1}{2}$ of D.

12. E is $\frac{1}{2}$ of B.

13. D is $\frac{1}{2}$ of G.

14. C, D and E are $\frac{1}{4}$ of ONE.

41

Page 42

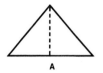 ### Problem Solving: 2

Use the 7 tangram pieces to answer the following questions.

1. The triangle shapes are __A__, __C__, __E__, __F__ and __G__.

2. The square shape is __B__.

3. The parallelogram shape is __D__.

4. How do triangles G and F compare? They are the same size and shape. They are congruent triangles

5. How do triangles C and E compare? They are the same size and shape. They are congruent triangles

6. Draw tangrams A, B and D using triangles C and E in the space below.

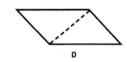

A   B

D

42

Page 43

Problem Solving: 3

Use the 7 tangram pieces to complete the following activities:

1. How many of the C shapes fit into the F shape? __4__

2. Would the same number of E shapes fit into the G shape? __yes__

How do you know? C and E are congruent shapes. F and G are congruent shapes. Four C or E will fit into F or G.

3. How would you "build" F or G by using B? You may use other tangram pieces to complete this task. Please show your work.

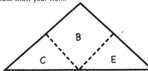

4. How would you "build" F or G by using D and other tangram pieces? You may use other tangram pieces to complete this task. Please show your work.

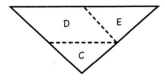

43

Page 44

Problem Solving: 4

Draw a square by using the two triangle pieces G and F and label it ONE.

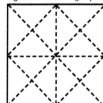

1. How many square tangram pieces will fit into this square? __4__

Each square is $\frac{1}{4}$ of ONE.

2. Use shapes A and D in the square. What other shape or shapes will be needed to fill in the square? 1B, 1C and 1E, or 1 more A, 1C and 1E.

3. D and A cover what part of ONE? $\frac{1}{2}$ or $\frac{4}{8}$ or $\frac{2}{4}$

4. How many C's and E's will cover ONE? 4 of each

5. How many C's would cover $\frac{1}{2}$ of ONE? __4__

44

Tangram Solutions

Problem Solving: 5

Use your tangram pieces and complete the following:

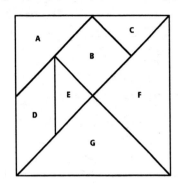

1. If there are 2 **C**'s in **A**, then there are ___2___ **E**'s in **A**.

2. If there are 2 **A**'s in **F**, then there are ___2___ **A**'s in **G**.

3. If there are 4 **E**'s in **G**, then there are ___4___ **E**'s in **F**.

4. If there are 4 **C**'s in **F**, then there are ___4___ **C**'s in **G**.

5. How many more **C**'s are in **F** than in **G**? ___0___

6. How many more **E**'s are in **A** than in **C**? ___1___

7. How many more **A**'s are in ONE than in **G**? ___6___

45

Problem Solving: 6

Use your tangram pieces and complete the following:

1. **E** is what part of **C**? ___=___

2. **B** is what part of **F**? ___$\frac{1}{2}$___

3. **G** is what part of ONE? ___$\frac{1}{4}$___

4. **A** is what part of **G** and **F**? ___$\frac{1}{2}$___

5. **E** is what part of **G** and **F**? ___$\frac{1}{4}$___

6. How many **C**'s are in **A**? ___2___   **C** is ___$\frac{1}{2}$___ of **A**.

7. How many **C**'s are in **B**? ___2___   **C** is ___$\frac{1}{2}$___ of **B**.

8. How many **C**'s are in **D**? ___2___   **C** is ___$\frac{1}{2}$___ of **D**.

9. How many **C**'s are in **E**? ___1___   **C** is ___$\frac{1}{1}$___ of **E**.

10. How many **C**'s are in **F**? ___4___   **C** is ___$\frac{1}{4}$___ of **F**.

11. How many **C**'s are in **G**? ___4___   **C** is ___$\frac{1}{4}$___ of **G**.

12. How many **C**'s are in ONE? ___16___   **C** is ___$\frac{1}{16}$___ of ONE.

13. How many **A**'s are in **F**? ___2___   **A** is ___$\frac{1}{2}$___ of **F**.

14. How many **A**'s are in **G**? ___2___   **A** is ___$\frac{1}{2}$___ of **G**.

15. How many **A**'s are in ONE? ___8___   **A** is ___$\frac{1}{8}$___ of ONE.

16. How many **F**'s are in ONE? ___4___   **F** is ___$\frac{1}{4}$___ of ONE.

46

Problem Solving: 7

Use the small triangle ◺S as the tangram unit to "measure" and name the fractions and their equivalence.

$$1 \triangle S = \frac{1}{16}$$

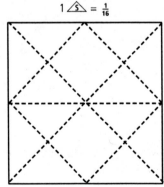

1. Triangle **A** = ___$\frac{2}{16}$___

2. Triangle **C** = ___$\frac{1}{16}$___

3. Square **B** = ___$\frac{2}{16}$___

4. Parallelogram **D** = ___$\frac{2}{16}$___

5. Triangle **E** = ___$\frac{1}{16}$___

6. Triangle **F** = ___$\frac{4}{16}$___

7. Triangle **G** = ___$\frac{4}{16}$___

8. Triangle **G** also = ___$\frac{2}{8}$___ and ___$\frac{1}{4}$___

9. Triangle **F** also = ___$\frac{2}{8}$___ and ___$\frac{1}{4}$___

10. Triangle **A** also = ___$\frac{1}{8}$___

11. Square **B** also = ___$\frac{1}{8}$___

12. Parallelogram **D** = ___$\frac{1}{8}$___

13. ONE = ___$\frac{16}{16}$___

47

1 This is One: 1

Use your tangram shapes to answer these questions.

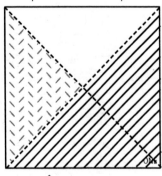

1. How many large triangles ◺L will cover ONE? ___4___

   Please draw each large triangle in ONE.

2. How many large triangles ◺L cover $\frac{1}{2}$ of ONE? ___2___

   Please color $\frac{1}{2}$ of ONE.

3. How many large triangles ◺L cover $\frac{1}{4}$ of ONE? ___1___

   Please color $\frac{1}{4}$ of ONE another color.

4. How many of the large triangles are colored? ___3___

5. How many of the large triangles are not colored? ___1___

48

Tangram Solutions

Page 49

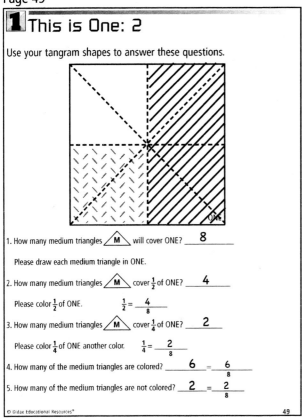

1 This is One: 2

Use your tangram shapes to answer these questions.

1. How many medium triangles ◺M will cover ONE? __8__

   Please draw each medium triangle in ONE.

2. How many medium triangles ◺M cover ½ of ONE? __4__

   Please color ½ of ONE.　　$\frac{1}{2} = \frac{4}{8}$

3. How many medium triangles ◺M cover ¼ of ONE? __2__

   Please color ¼ of ONE another color.　$\frac{1}{4} = \frac{2}{8}$

4. How many of the medium triangles are colored? __6__ $= \frac{6}{8}$

5. How many of the medium triangles are not colored? __2__ $= \frac{2}{8}$

　　　49

Page 50

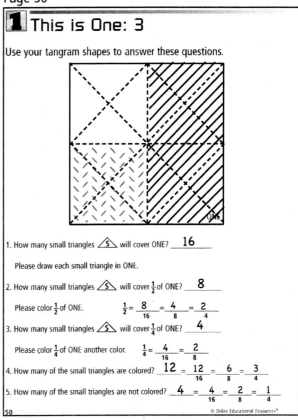

1 This is One: 3

Use your tangram shapes to answer these questions.

1. How many small triangles ◺S will cover ONE? __16__

   Please draw each small triangle in ONE.

2. How many small triangles ◺S will cover ½ of ONE? __8__

   Please color ½ of ONE.　　$\frac{1}{2} = \frac{8}{16} = \frac{4}{8} = \frac{2}{4}$

3. How many small triangles ◺S will cover ¼ of ONE? __4__

   Please color ¼ of ONE another color.　$\frac{1}{4} = \frac{4}{16} = \frac{2}{8}$

4. How many of the small triangles are colored? __12__ $= \frac{12}{16} = \frac{6}{8} = \frac{3}{4}$

5. How many of the small triangles are not colored? __4__ $= \frac{4}{16} = \frac{2}{8} = \frac{1}{4}$

50　

Page 51

1 This is One: 4

Use your tangram shapes to answer these questions.

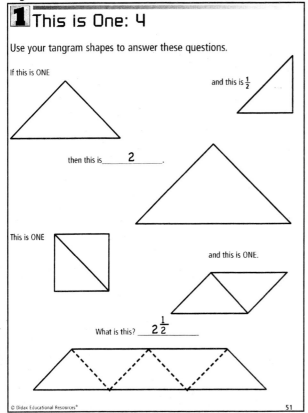

If this is ONE

and this is ½

then this is __2__.

This is ONE

and this is ONE.

What is this? __$2\frac{1}{2}$__

　　　51

Page 52

1 This is One: 5

Use your tangram shapes to answer these questions.

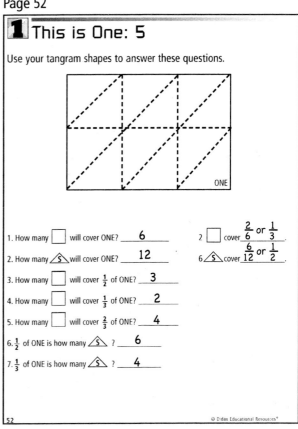

1. How many ☐ will cover ONE? __6__

2. How many ◺S will cover ONE? __12__

3. How many ☐ will cover ½ of ONE? __3__

4. How many ☐ will cover ⅓ of ONE? __2__

5. How many ☐ will cover ⅔ of ONE? __4__

6. ½ of ONE is how many ◺S ? __6__

7. ⅓ of ONE is how many ◺S ? __4__

2 ☐ cover $\frac{2}{6}$ or $\frac{1}{3}$.

6 ◺S cover $\frac{6}{12}$ or $\frac{1}{2}$.

52

Tangram Solutions

1 This is One: 6

Use your tangram pieces and name these fractions:

8. Each ⟋S⟍ is what part of ONE? $\frac{1}{12}$

9. Each ☐ is what part of ONE? $\frac{1}{6}$

10. Two ⟋S⟍ are equal to what part of ONE? $\frac{2}{12}$ or $\frac{1}{6}$

11. Three ☐ are equal to what part of ONE? $\frac{3}{6}$ or $\frac{1}{2}$

12. Please look at ONE and rename these fractions.

   a. $\frac{3}{6}$ is another name for $\frac{1}{2}$.

   b. $\frac{2}{6}$ is another name for $\frac{1}{3}$.

   c. $\frac{4}{12}$ is another name for $\frac{1}{3}$ or $\frac{2}{6}$.

   d. $\frac{6}{12}$ is another name for $\frac{1}{2}$ or $\frac{3}{6}$.

   e. $\frac{1}{6} = \frac{2}{12}$

   f. $\frac{3}{6} = \frac{6}{12}$

   g. $\frac{4}{12} = \frac{2}{6}$

   h. $\frac{1}{2} = \frac{6}{12} = \frac{3}{6}$

   i. $\frac{1}{3} = \frac{2}{6} = \frac{4}{12}$

   j. $\frac{2}{3} = \frac{4}{6} = \frac{8}{12}$

   k. $\frac{6}{6} = \frac{12}{12}$

53